NEEDED

QUICK
Affirmations
JOURNAL

FOR NOT-SO-EASY DAYS

BALANCED

Influential

Magnificent

ROCK

Be well!
XOXO
Kim Ann

Written by
Kim Ann and **Yobe Qiu**

Illustrated by
Nejla Shojaie

Welcome!

We hope you had a chance to read one of our Quick Affirmation books or have enjoyed one of our card sets. One of our readers once told us he felt like he could "charge through a wall" after reading our book. We thought it might be more impactful if you had a journal to write down your thoughts or a means to process through a not-so-easy day, so, we created this for you.

We are super busy people, just like you, so we know the importance of taking a moment to jot down a few thoughts and how this is key to a positive growth mindset.

With this journal we hope you will take a moment to reflect and refocus. Use this as an effective tool for recharging so you can continue on with your busy day refreshed. While journaling, remember to be gentle to yourself and also document your strengths; this will help you get through a difficult moment or thought and bring your "A" game to the forefront.

Happy Journaling

Yobe & Kim

I **Appreciate** MYSELF AND **Acknowledge** MY STRENGTHS.

Affirmations

_____

_____

_____

_____

_____

_____

_____

_____

_____

_____

_____

_____

_____

_____

Affirmations

_____

_____

_____

_____

_____

_____

_____

_____

_____

_____

_____

_____

_____

_____

Affirmations

_____

_____

_____

_____

_____

_____

_____

_____

_____

_____

_____

_____

Affirmations

_____

_____

_____

_____

_____

_____

_____

_____

_____

_____

_____

_____

_____

I AM

Balanced

AND

Bold.

Affirmations

Affirmations

_____

_____

_____

_____

_____

_____

_____

_____

_____

_____

_____

_____

_____

_____

Affirmations

Affirmations

_____

_____

_____

_____

_____

_____

_____

_____

_____

_____

_____

_____

_____

_____

I *Elevate* MYSELF AND OTHERS ALONG THE WAY.

Affirmations

Affirmations

_____

_____

_____

_____

_____

_____

_____

_____

_____

_____

_____

_____

_____

Affirmations

Affirmations

_____

_____

_____

_____

_____

_____

_____

_____

_____

_____

_____

_____

_____

_____

I AM Forgiving OF MYSELF.

Affirmations

_____

_____

_____

_____

_____

_____

_____

_____

_____

_____

_____

_____

_____

Affirmations

_____

_____

_____

_____

_____

_____

_____

_____

_____

_____

_____

_____

_____

_____

Affirmations

_____

_____

_____

_____

_____

_____

_____

_____

_____

_____

_____

_____

_____

_____

Affirmations

I AM
Important,
INSIGHTFUL,
AND
Influential.

Affirmations

_____

_____

_____

_____

_____

_____

_____

_____

_____

_____

_____

_____

_____

_____

Affirmations

_____

_____

_____

_____

_____

_____

_____

_____

_____

_____

_____

_____

_____

_____

Affirmations

_____

_____

_____

_____

_____

_____

_____

_____

_____

_____

_____

_____

_____

Affirmations

_____

_____

_____

_____

_____

_____

_____

_____

_____

_____

_____

_____

_____

_____

_____

_____

I AM
Judicious
IN MY Journey.

Affirmations

_____

_____

_____

_____

_____

_____

_____

_____

_____

_____

_____

_____

_____

_____

Affirmations

_____

_____

_____

_____

_____

_____

_____

_____

_____

_____

_____

_____

_____

Affirmations

_____

_____

_____

_____

_____

_____

_____

_____

_____

_____

_____

_____

_____

Affirmations

_____

_____

_____

_____

_____

_____

_____

_____

_____

_____

_____

_____

_____

I AM
Motivated,
MAGNETIC,
AND
Magnificent.

Affirmations

_____

_____

_____

_____

_____

_____

_____

_____

_____

_____

_____

_____

Affirmations

_____

_____

_____

_____

_____

_____

_____

_____

_____

_____

_____

_____

_____

_____

Affirmations

_____

_____

_____

_____

_____

_____

_____

_____

_____

_____

_____

_____

_____

_____

Affirmations

_____

_____

_____

_____

_____

_____

_____

_____

_____

_____

_____

_____

_____

I AM

Noble,

NOTEWORTHY,

AND

Needed.

Affirmations

_____

_____

_____

_____

_____

_____

_____

_____

_____

_____

_____

_____

_____

_____

Affirmations

Affirmations

_____

_____

_____

_____

_____

_____

_____

_____

_____

_____

_____

_____

_____

_____

_____

_____

Affirmations

Affirmations

_____

_____

_____

_____

_____

_____

_____

_____

_____

_____

_____

_____

_____

_____

Affirmations

_____

_____

_____

_____

_____

_____

_____

_____

_____

_____

_____

_____

_____

Affirmations

Affirmations

_____

_____

_____

_____

_____

_____

_____

_____

_____

_____

_____

_____

_____

_____

I AM

Resilient

AND A

Rock FOR THOSE

I LOVE.

Affirmations

_____

_____

_____

_____

_____

_____

_____

_____

_____

_____

_____

_____

_____

Affirmations

_____

_____

_____

_____

_____

_____

_____

_____

_____

_____

_____

_____

_____

_____

Affirmations

_____

_____

_____

_____

_____

_____

_____

_____

_____

_____

_____

_____

_____

Affirmations

_____

_____

_____

_____

_____

_____

_____

_____

_____

_____

_____

_____

_____

I SAY

"Yes,"

TO THE THINGS I WANT.

Affirmations

_____

_____

_____

_____

_____

_____

_____

_____

_____

_____

_____

_____

_____

_____

Affirmations

_____

_____

_____

_____

_____

_____

_____

_____

_____

_____

_____

_____

_____

_____

Affirmations

Affirmations

_____

_____

_____

_____

_____

_____

_____

_____

_____

_____

_____

_____

_____

_____

I AM *Zen*

AND I AM AT PEACE.

Affirmations

_____

_____

_____

_____

_____

_____

_____

_____

_____

_____

_____

_____

_____

Affirmations

_____

_____

_____

_____

_____

_____

_____

_____

_____

_____

_____

_____

_____

_____

Affirmations

_____

_____

_____

_____

_____

_____

_____

_____

_____

_____

_____

_____

_____

_____

NEEDED

JUDICIOUS

Important

Forgiving

Yes

BALANCED

Journey

ACKNOWLEDGE

Motivated

RESILIENT

Noble

Influential

Elevate

BOLD

Magnificent

Question

APPRECIATE

OTHER BOOK TITLES IN THE
Quick Affirmations Series

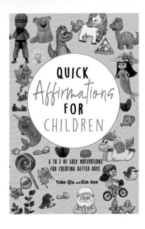

AFFIRMATION CARDS AND MERCHANDISE AVAILABLE

luckyfourpress.com
#QuickAffirmations